IMPORTANT SAFETY
INSTRUCTIONS

While the **Publisher** has used all reasonable endeavours to ensure that these experiments are safe for children to undertake, there are some that require the **assistance of a grown-up**. These are marked with . . .

. . . in the stages of each experiment concerned.

Young scientists, please make use of your grown-ups, and **don't try these alone**! Stick to the steps described in this book for **maximum safety** and the **best results**.

ROALD DAHL was a spy, ace fighter pilot, chocolate historian and medical inventor. He was also the author of *Charlie and the Chocolate Factory, Matilda, The BFG* and many more brilliant stories. He remains THE WORLD'S NUMBER ONE STORYTELLER.

QUENTIN BLAKE has illustrated more than three hundred books and was Roald Dahl's favourite illustrator. In 1980 he won the prestigious Kate Greenaway Medal. In 1999 he became the first ever Children's Laureate and in 2013 he was knighted for services to illustration.

ROALD DAHL'S

GEORGE'S MARVELLOUS EXPERIMENTS

Illustrated by QUENTIN BLAKE

PUFFIN

PUFFIN BOOKS

UK | USA | Canada | Ireland | Australia
India | New Zealand | South Africa

Puffin Books is part of the Penguin Random House group of companies
whose addresses can be found at global.penguinrandomhouse.com.

www.penguin.co.uk
www.puffin.co.uk
www.ladybird.co.uk

First published 2017

001

Written by Barry Hutchison

Thanks to Michelle Porte Davies and Sarah Topping

Printed in Italy

A CIP catalogue record for this book is available from the British Library

ISBN: 978–0–141–37594–6

All correspondence to:
Puffin Books
Penguin Random House Children's
80 Strand, London WC2R 0RL

MIX
Paper from
responsible sources
FSC® C018179

Penguin Random House is committed to a
sustainable future for our business, our readers
and our planet. This book is made from Forest
Stewardship Council® certified paper.

CONTENTS

INTRODUCTION

WELCOME to **George's Marvellous Experiments**, inspired by Roald Dahl's *George's Marvellous Medicine*. In this rather **brilliant tale**, George Kranky has had enough of his **grizzly old grunion of a grandma**, with her pale brown teeth and small puckered-up mouth like a **dog's bottom**. Most grandmas are kind and lovely ladies, but George's grandma is a **miserable old grouch**. In fact, George isn't entirely sure that she isn't a witch.

ONE DAY, George decides to **teach her a lesson**. He wants to **invent a medicine** that will blow off the top of her head! Using the **magic of science** and many wondrous ingredients, like WAXWELL FLOOR POLISH and FLEA POWDER FOR DOGS and FLOWERS OF TURNIPS, George concocts the most **marvellous medicine** in the world – with astonishing results . . .

NOW, this book might not make your grandma go through the roof or make your chickens lay football-sized eggs, but you can expect **explosions**, **eruptions**, **squelches**, **stinks** and much, much more.

SO PREPARE to **discover the wonders of science** (and be sure to ask a grown-up to help you with the trickier bits!).

It's going to be **MARVELLOUS**!

CHAPTER ONE
MARVELLOUSLY
MESSY

'What **MISCHIEF** are you up to in there now?' GRANNY **SCREECHED**. 'I hear NOISES.'

Are you ready to get **stuck in**?
The only way to be an **inventor** like George is to throw in **EVERYTHING** and see what happens.
It's so much **fun** that way . . .

MAKE YOUR OWN VOLCANIC ERUPTION

George hates Grandma so much that he wants to do something about her. Something **whopping**, a sort of **explosion** . . . and here's how you can make your own **giant eruption**!

 This one can get **very messy very quickly**, so either do it **outside** or build your volcano on a baking tray or large dish.

WHAT TO DO:

1

Take the lid off an **empty plastic bottle** and stand it on a flat, **level surface**. Use the **modelling clay** to **cover the bottle**. Try to make it look volcano-shaped, and don't forget to leave an **opening at the top** so the lava can erupt out of it.

2

In a bowl, **mix together** half a bottle of **vinegar** with some **red food colouring**. Add a squirt of **washing-up liquid** and stir.

3

Carefully pour the vinegar mixture into the bottle through the hole at the top of the volcano.

4

Wrap two or three heaped tablespoons of bicarbonate of soda in a sheet of **kitchen roll** or tissue.

Tie the package together with **elastic bands** so the powder can't leak out.

5

Drop the package into the volcano – then **stand back**. Marvel at the **spluttering, fizzing** 'lava' as it fizzes and splutters through the hole at the top, just like **a real volcano** (only not as hot).

WHAT IF?

Try cutting the top off the bottle to make a **wider hole**. **How does this affect the eruption?**

What happens if you **leave out** the washing-up liquid?

WHAT'S HAPPENING HERE:

Bicarbonate of soda is another name for the chemical sodium bicarbonate. This is an **alkaline** that, when mixed with the **acetic acid** in the vinegar, creates carbon dioxide gas – just like in our **Foaming Fizzy Potion** experiment (see pages 6–7). Although it's a 'greenhouse gas', carbon dioxide is otherwise completely harmless and is used to put the fizz in soft drinks.

MAKE YOUR OWN
PUTTY
FARM

There are lots of methods for making **squidgy silly putty** that you can shape and mould, but most involve **weird chemicals** that are better used for **unblocking drains** or feeding to **miserable old grandmas** (but not your grandma!). This version is completely cleaning-product free and you can make your putty farm animals as **GIANT** or tiny as you want, just like George did.

WHAT TO DO:

1

Put **two cups** of **flour** in a big mixing bowl.

2

Crack in the eggs and **mix them** all together. Try not to think about cakes. Once the mixture is **smooth, stir** in **three quarters of a cup** of the glue, a little bit at a time.

3

Mix, mix, mix. Mix a bit more, **slowly** adding a few tablespoons of water until the mixture turns **putty-like**.

4

Add some **drops** of your chosen **food colouring** and mix it in. Use your hands to really **squish** the colour in there.

WHAT'S HAPPENING HERE:

With the **flour**, **eggs** and **water**, you're actually making a basic **dough**. The **glue** acts as a **binding agent**, which holds the mixture together, creating a malleable putty that can be **stretched**, **shaped**, **squashed** and **bounced**.

WHAT IF?

What happens if you use **half** as much **glue**?

What if you use **twice as much**?

FOAMING FIZZY POTION

When George made his marvellous medicine, it **frothed** and **fizzed** and **foamed** as if it were alive! Now you can re-create that same effect for yourself and concoct something that looks like a **weird magic potion**.

WHAT YOU'LL NEED:

- Bicarbonate of soda
- A plastic cup or mug
- Washing-up liquid
- Food colouring (optional)
- Lemon juice

WHAT TO DO:

1

Put a **teaspoon** of the **bicarbonate of soda** into the cup. Any cup will do, but tall, narrow ones work best.

2

Add a **squirt** of washing-up liquid.

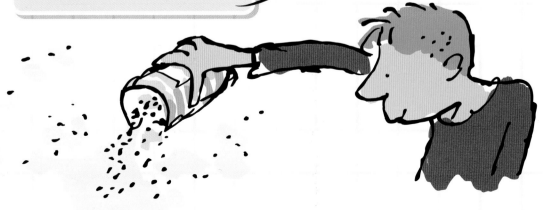

3

Stir to mix together. If it's tricky to stir with a spoon, try using a long drinking straw.

If you want your magic potion to be **colourful** (and who wouldn't?), add some **food colouring**. Not too much – a couple of drops will do.

4

Squeeze or **pour** in a small amount of **lemon juice. Continue stirring while you pour.** As you stir, **bubbles** will form and start to fill the cup!

5

Add more **lemon juice** and **bicarbonate of soda** until the **frothy mixture** bubbles up over the top!

WHAT IF?

Try using another citrus fruit juice like **lime** or **orange**. Do they have the same effect?

What happens if you use a **large bowl** instead of a cup?

WHAT'S HAPPENING HERE:

The **bicarbonate of soda**, when mixed with the **lemon juice**, is forming **carbon dioxide gas.** As this fizzes up in the washing-up liquid, it creates lots of soapy bubbles – see, **science IS magic!**

GOOEY, GUNGY GLOOP

Grandma is a real **old hag**. She's **filthy** and **disgusting**! Now you can make something really unpleasant, just like her!

WHAT TO DO:

1

Very carefully, pour **boiling water** into the mug until it is about **half full**.

Add **three teaspoons** of **gelatin** to the mug.

2

Wait **twenty** to **thirty seconds**. Perhaps use this time to fondly remember the **biggest bit of gungy gloop** you've ever seen.

3

Using a **fork**, give the mixture a **stir**. Add one or two drops of the **food colouring**.

4

Add **syrup** until the mug is roughly **two thirds full**, then give it another **stir**.

5

Slowly add cold water until you achieve that **perfect gooey consistency**.

WHAT IF?

What if you use **powdered jelly mixture** instead of gelatin?

How about if you **replace the syrup** with some **sugar** in boiling water?

WHAT'S HAPPENING HERE:

The snot produced inside your head is a mixture of **protein** and **sugar**, which is more or less what you've just mixed in your mug. The long, **stringy bits** are **protein strands**, and they're what give both the real and fake stuff its **amazing stretchiness**!

BOOGIE GLOOP

Grandma's voice isn't soft and lovely – she's **shrill** and **shouty**! Here's how you can make your own **glorious gloop** and see **invisible sound waves** in action. It's **messy**, it's **fun** – it's **two experiments in one**!

WHAT YOU'LL NEED:
- A mixing bowl
- Cornflour
- Water
- A subwoofer music speaker
- A thin metal baking tray
- Food colouring (optional)

WHAT TO DO:

1

Mix two cups of cornflour with **half a cup** of water. Add more water until your gloop is thick and ... well, **gloopy**. Add some spots of **food colouring** if you like.

2

Lay the music speaker on its back and place the metal tray **over the part where the sound comes out.**

3

Pour your gloop on to the tray.

4

Press lightly on one corner of the tray to hold it steady.

Play music through the speaker – **the louder, the better.**

5

Your gloop should start to **jiggle** and **dance** on the tray. If it doesn't, try a different song, change the volume or adjust the pressure you're putting on the tray.

WHAT IF?

What makes the gloop dance more – **low frequencies** or **high frequencies**?

Try changing the mixture. Does **thicker gloop** dance better than **thinner**?

WHAT'S HAPPENING HERE:

When at rest, the cornflour and water mixture is mostly liquid. **When agitated**, though, it becomes more firm and almost solid. As the sound waves pass through the gloop, the **vibrations alter the consistency**, turning it from **solid to liquid** and back again, and making it jiggle and wiggle around on the tray.

QUICKER THAN QUICKSAND

When Grandma drinks her **marvellous medicine**, she grows quicker than you'd ever believe – one minute she's in her chair, the next she's **through the roof**! Quicksand can be pretty **magical stuff**, too. Is it a **liquid**? Is it a **solid**? Is it both? Let's make some and find out.

WHAT TO DO:

1 **Pour** one good-sized cup of **cornflour** into your container.

2 Add **half** as much **water**. **Mix it up.**

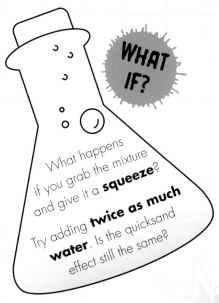

WHAT IF?

What happens if you grab the mixture and give it a **squeeze**? Try adding **twice as much water**. Is the quicksand effect still the same?

WHAT'S HAPPENING HERE:

This **quicksand** is similar to the **dancing gloop** on pages 10–11. If you **stir the mixture slowly**, it stays liquid-like. This is because the water is able to flow between the cornflour grains fairly easily. **Stir it quickly**, though, and the grains have no room to move, so they get **stuck together**, turning the mixture thick, clumpy and almost solid. Try jabbing a pencil into it to see your quicksand **instantly harden** in that one spot. If you want to **really** impress people, you can tell them that this is an example of a **non-Newtonian fluid**, which defies the laws of (Newtonian) physics.

CHAPTER TWO
EXCELLENT ERUPTIONS

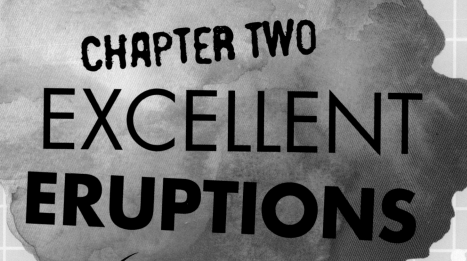

'Will she go **POP**?
Will she **EXPLODE**?
Will she go **FLYING**
    down the ROAD?
Will she go **POOF**
    in a **PUFF** of SMOKE?
Start **FIZZING** like
    a can of Coke?'

George has no way of knowing quite how explosive his medicine will be – but Grandma soon finds out, with very exciting consequences!

BAG-GO-BOOM!

WHAT YOU'LL NEED:
- Bicarbonate of soda
- Kitchen roll or toilet tissue
- White vinegar
- A ziplock sandwich bag
- Warm water

Grandma suspects George is up to **mischief** when she hears **noises** from the kitchen – but she could never guess how much mischief he's brewing! **Have a blast** (literally) by trying this completely safe – but brilliantly noisy – **explosive experiment**.

> ⚠️ Things will get **messy** with this one, so it's best to do it **outside**, and to **wear old clothes**.

WHAT TO DO:

1 Place a **tablespoon** of **bicarbonate of soda** on a sheet of kitchen roll (or a couple of sheets of toilet tissue) and **twist it into a packet**.

2 Pour **half a cup of vinegar** into the **bag**.

3

Add around **half as much warm water as you did vinegar**. Zip up the bag, leaving **just enough room** for you to squeeze your **packet of bicarbonate of soda** in through the gap.

4

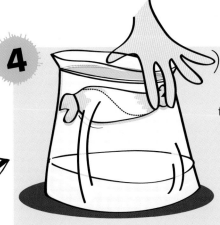

This is where it gets a bit tricky. **Push** the packet into the bag, but **squeeze the bag** so the bicarbonate of soda **doesn't drop into the liquid**. Zip the bag the rest of the way up, making sure there are **no gaps**.

5

Give the bag a **quick shake** so the kitchen roll or toilet tissue gets wet.

Drop and retreat – then watch the bag expand until it goes **POP!**

WHAT IF?

What if you don't put **water** into the **vinegar mixture**?

What if you put your **bag inside another bag**, which also contains a vinegar mixture, **before** letting the bicarbonate of soda fall in?

WHAT'S HAPPENING HERE:

This is **carbon dioxide** at work again. In previous experiments, the gas was able to escape freely into the air. In this experiment we've **trapped it**; so, when the reaction between the **sodium bicarbonate** and the **acetic acid** takes place, the gas rapidly fills the bag until there's no more space inside.

FLYING FILM CANISTER

Just a spoonful of **George's** concoction sends one of his dad's **chickens** straight up into the air like a **rocket**! This is one of the simplest rocket-type experiments, but the results are pretty **spectacular** (with no chickens required!).

WHAT YOU'LL NEED:

- Safety goggles
- An Alka-Seltzer or similar fizzing antacid tablet
- An empty 35mm plastic film canister with lid (find them in camera shops)
- A glass of water

 Always do this one **outside** where you have **plenty of space** for your rocket to fly.

WHAT TO DO:

1

Put on your **safety goggles**. You really don't want the flying film canister to hit you in the eye.

Break the **antacid tablet** in two.

2

Take the **lid off** the film canister and tip in a **teaspoonful of water**. From here on, everything is going to happen very fast, so make sure any **spectators** are standing **two to three metres away**.

3

Drop in **half a tablet** and **VERY QUICKLY** replace the canister lid. You should hear a snapping sound to let you know it's secure.

WHAT'S HAPPENING HERE:

When the **antacid tablet** mixes with the **water**, it begins to create **carbon dioxide gas**. As the reaction continues, more and more of the gas is created, building **pressure** inside the canister. Eventually, the pressure becomes **too great** and the **lid is forced off**. Because the lid is against the ground and has nowhere to go, the rest of the canister **launches into the air**.

4

Place the canister on the ground **upside-down**, so the lid is at the bottom. **Quickly stand back.**

WHAT IF?

What happens if you use a **whole tablet** or change the **amount of water**?

What if you **don't turn** the canister upside-down when placing it on the ground?

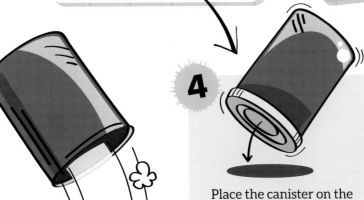

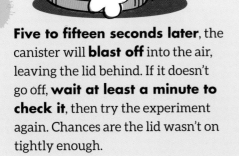

5

Five to fifteen seconds later, the canister will **blast off** into the air, leaving the lid behind. If it doesn't go off, **wait at least a minute to check it**, then try the experiment again. Chances are the lid wasn't on tightly enough.

SPECTACULAR SONIC BLASTER

WHAT YOU'LL NEED:

- A cardboard tube (the tube from a toilet roll is ideal)
- Stiff paper or card
- Scissors
- A sharp pencil
- Sticky tape
- Thin plastic (try cutting up a sandwich bag)
- An elastic band
- Some fluff (or other light object)

Sound waves are constantly **whizzing** through the air, just like that chicken after a dose of **Grandma's medicine**! However, we can't hear them until they bump into our **eardrums** and make them **vibrate**. A big enough **sound wave** can even **move objects**, as this experiment will demonstrate.

WHAT TO DO:

1

Cut a circle of the paper or card that's the **same size** as the opening in your **cardboard tube**. The easiest way to do this is to draw round the tube first.

2

Using the **pencil**, make a **small hole in the centre** of your circle of paper or card.

3

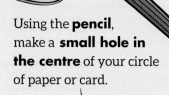

Tape the circle to one end of the **tube**, being careful **not to cover** the hole you made. Make sure there are **no gaps** around the join (use more tape, if necessary).

4

Cut a piece of **thin plastic** and place it over the **other end of the tube**. Use the **elastic band** to fix it in place. Make sure the plastic is stretched nice and **tightly**.

5

Aim the **end of the tube with the hole** in it at the **fluff**. **Tap** the plastic and watch the fluff move. The harder you tap it, the further your **fluff will fly!**

WHAT IF?

What happens if you try moving a **heavier object**?

Does a **longer tube** make the sound blaster **more** or **less powerful**?

WHAT'S HAPPENING HERE:

When your **fingers drum** on the tightly stretched plastic, it **generates sound**. The **sound rushes down the tube** and, as it has nowhere else to go, it gets **compressed** through the **small hole**. Being compressed makes the **sound wave powerful** enough to move objects in its path.

FIGHT FIRE WITH FIZZ

WHAT YOU'LL NEED:

- A grown-up
- A small candle
- A glass jar or dish
- Modelling clay
- Bicarbonate of soda
- Vinegar

After **George** gives **Grandma** her medicine, she thinks her **stomach's on fire**! 'I'll be fried to a frizzle!' she cries. 'I'll be boiled like a beetroot!' Grandma needs **extinguishing – fast**! Now, vinegar and bicarbonate of soda can be used to make things go **bang**, but they can also be used to **stop fire spreading**.

Ask a **grown-up** to help you turn these everyday ingredients into a **magic fire-extinguisher**.

WHAT TO DO:

1

Stand the **candle upright** in the **bottom of the glass**, using the modelling clay to hold it in place. The candle must be short enough that it **doesn't stick out above the glass**.

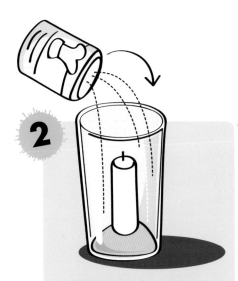

2

Sprinkle bicarbonate of soda all over the **bottom of the glass** around the candle.

3

⚠️

Ask a grown-up to light the candle.

4

Using a **spoon**, **dribble some vinegar** over the **bicarbonate of soda. Not too much** – you don't want to cover the candle.

5

As the bicarbonate of soda and vinegar react together, the **candle flame goes out**, as if by **magic**!

WHAT'S HAPPENING HERE:

Fire needs **oxygen to burn**, so as the glass fills with **carbon dioxide gas** the **oxygen** is pushed up and **out of the glass**. Without oxygen, the flame can't survive, and so it is snuffed out.

WHAT IF?

Ask a **grown-up** to try lighting the candle again, **after it has been snuffed out**. What happens?

What happens if you use a candle that's **taller than the glass**?

MARVELLOUSLY MINTY GEYSER

WHAT YOU'LL NEED:
- A large bottle of diet cola
- Thin card or stiff paper
- A packet of Mentos mints
- Quick reflexes!

WHAT TO DO:

George can't be sure what will happen when Grandma **drinks the mixture**, but anything is possible! Will she go **flying** down the road? Will she go **poof** in a **puff of smoke**? Start **fizzing** like a can of Coke? This is one experiment that calls for cola – and lots of space outside! You may want to put on your **waterproofs** and have an **umbrella** on standby before you attempt this **enormously explosive experiment**.

⚠

Do not, under any circumstances, try this one **indoors**, or **the room will never be the same again**.

1

Place your bottle **upright** in an **outside space**, with **plenty of room on all sides (especially above)**.

22

2

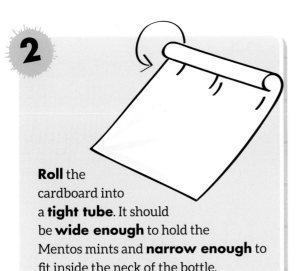

Roll the cardboard into a **tight tube**. It should be **wide enough** to hold the Mentos mints and **narrow enough** to fit inside the neck of the bottle.

3

Remove the mints from their packet and line them up in the tube, **keeping your finger over the hole** at the bottom to stop them from falling out.

4

Place the **end** of the tube **over** the **top** of the bottle.

Remove your finger, allowing all the mints to fall into the bottle. **Run for cover** as the diet cola shoots high into the air, then rains down on top of you.

WHAT'S HAPPENING HERE:

Scientists are actually quite **puzzled** as to why the Mentos mints and diet cola react together the way they do. Previously, they believed it was a **chemical reaction**, but now they think the **reaction is physical**. When the mints are dropped into the fizzy drink, their **pitted surface collects lots of carbon dioxide molecules**. As they **sink** to the bottom, the **carbon dioxide is released all at once** and goes rushing upwards towards the open spout.

WHAT IF?

What happens if you use a **different type of fizzy drink**?

What if you put the Mentos mints in **one at a time**?

Turn to **page 28** for another use for your mints and cola!

BOTTLE TOP POP

Create a **high-powered bottle-top launcher** using just a standard plastic water bottle, your hands and quite a lot of **muscle-power**!

WHAT YOU'LL NEED:
- An empty plastic water bottle
- Strong fingers

WHAT TO DO:

1 Take your **empty bottle** and put the lid on so it's **reasonably tight**. Grip the top half of the bottle in one hand and the bottom half in the other. **Point away from your face** (or anyone else's face, for that matter).

2 **Twist** both halves in **opposite directions**. Keep twisting for as long as you can.

3 Once the bottle **can't be twisted** any further, very **slowly open the cap**.

4 **BOOM!** The cap will **shoot off and fly** several metres through the air.

WHAT'S HAPPENING HERE:

The more you **twist the bottle**, the more **compressed the air inside it** becomes. Once you've reached the point where you can't twist it any further, all that air is desperately looking for a way to **escape**. As soon as you **loosen the lid**, all that compressed air rushes to escape and the **lid is fired off at high speed**.

WHAT IF?

What happens to the bottle once the lid has shot off?

Did you notice anything unusual about the **air inside** the bottle after it has **popped**?

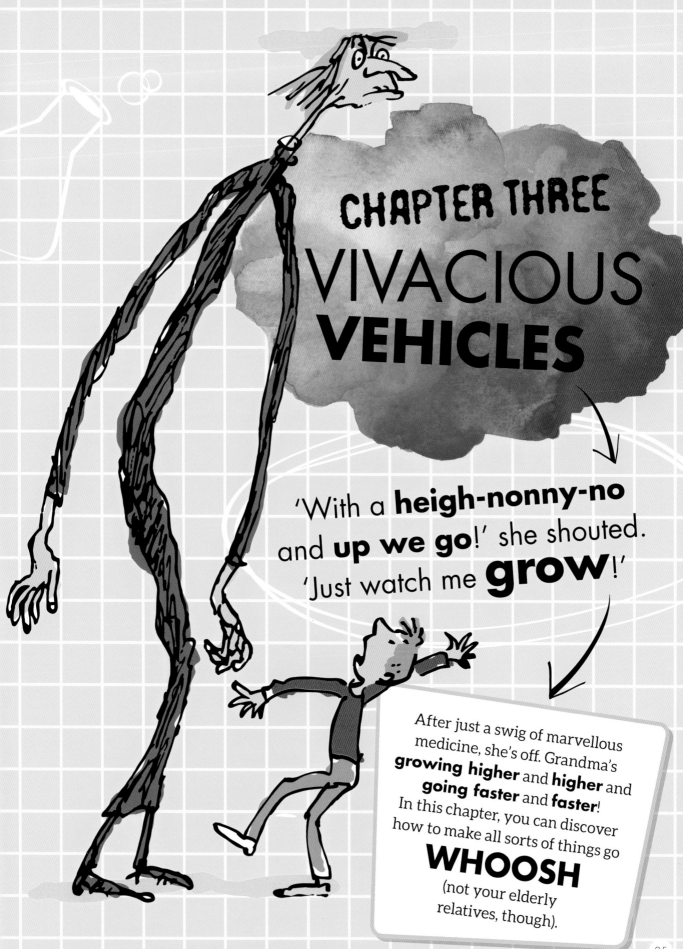

CHAPTER THREE
VIVACIOUS VEHICLES

'With a **heigh-nonny-no** and **up we go**!' she shouted. 'Just watch me **grow**!'

After just a swig of marvellous medicine, she's off. Grandma's **growing higher** and **higher** and **going faster** and **faster**! In this chapter, you can discover how to make all sorts of things go **WHOOSH** (not your elderly relatives, though).

JOLLY JET BALLOON

WHAT YOU'LL NEED:

- Long piece of string
- Straight drinking straw
- Sticky tape
- Balloon

From **racing cars** to **high-speed aircraft**, the **fastest vehicles** in the world are almost always **powered by jet engines**. This simple version will demonstrate how these engines **whoosh** through the air faster than a medicine-fuelled miserable old grandma.

WHAT TO DO:

1

First, feed the **string** through the **drinking straw**.

2

Pick **two walls** on **opposite sides of a room** and cut the string so it's a **few centimetres longer** than the distance between these walls.

3

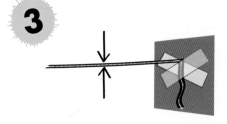

Tape one end of the string to the wall at your **start** point, and the other to your **end** point. Make sure it's quite **tight**, with **no sagging** in the middle.

4

Inflate the balloon until it's as **full** as it can go without bursting but **don't tie the end**! Holding the end of the balloon, use **sticky tape** to attach it to the straw.

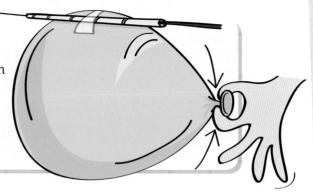

5

Slide the balloon and straw back to the beginning of the string. **Let go** and watch as the balloon shoots across the room at **high speed**.

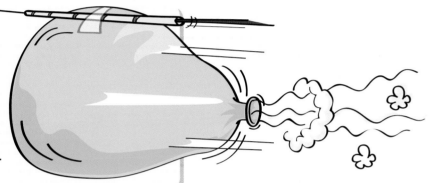

WHAT IF?

What if you **don't attach** the balloon to the straw and thread?

How about attaching **one end** of the string to the **floor** and the other to the **ceiling**?

WHAT'S HAPPENING HERE:

Jet engines work by **sucking in air** at the **front**, **superheating** it, then forcing it out of the **back again**. This propels the **vehicle forward**, which is more or less what's happening here. The air leaves the balloon with such force that it sends the balloon shooting off in the **opposite direction** until all the air – or fuel – runs out.

BARMY BOTTLE ROCKET

WHAT YOU'LL NEED:
- A large bottle of diet cola
- A packet of Mentos mints
- Masking tape
- Safety goggles
- Lots (and lots) of empty space
- Old clothes and shoes

In the previous chapter, we discovered the delights of **dropping Mentos mints into a bottle of diet cola**, just as George discovered the delights of dropping **EVERYTHING** he could find into an **enormous saucepan** to brew **Grandma's magic medicine**! Let's see if we can use all that **explosive power** to launch our very own **bottle rocket**.

As with that previous experiment, this one should **only ever be conducted outside**.

WHAT TO DO:

1 Take the **lid off** your bottle and **set it aside**.

2 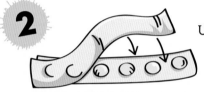 Use **two** or **three strips** of **masking tape** to make a **holder** for six or seven Mentos mints. Make sure there is a **gap on either side of each mint** to allow the cola to mix with the mints.

3

Tape the Mentos holder to the **inside** of the cola bottle lid. Make sure it's **nice and secure. Put on your safety goggles**. You're definitely going to need these.

4

Pour out some of the cola so that there is **enough room** to place the Mentos at the top of the bottle – the **mints must not come into contact with the cola (yet!)**. Carefully screw the lid – with the Mentos holder attached – back on the bottle. Make it **reasonably tight**, but don't tighten it all the way.

5

Shake the bottle vigorously. Throw it as **high** and as **far away** as possible. Watch the bottle **rocket** into the air, **zoom** along the ground, or **bounce** around madly, depending on how it landed.

WHAT IF?

What if you use **fruit-flavoured Mentos** instead of mint ones?

Does it make a **difference** if the cola is **cold** or **warm**?

WHAT'S HAPPENING HERE:

Just as with the **Marvellously Minty Geyser** on pages 22–23, all the **carbon dioxide** is rushing to **escape the bottle**. This time, though, the **pressure** in the bottle has a chance to **build up** before the top comes off, which **forces the cola out** at a much higher speed, **propelling** the bottle in the **opposite direction**.

SURPRISINGLY SIMPLE **MAGNETIC CAR**

WHAT YOU'LL NEED:
- Card
- An empty matchbox
- Two magnets
- Drinking straw
- Sticky tape
- Two cocktail sticks
- Scissors

We'll look at **magnets** in more detail in Chapter Five, but for now you can make your own **small magnetic car**, using a couple of magnets to **steer it** on a flat surface **without touching it**.

WHAT TO DO:

1

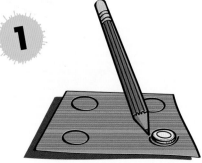

Make the wheels for your car by **drawing four circles** on the card and cutting them out. **Draw round a pound coin** to make sure they're all the same size.

2 Tape one of the magnets **inside the matchbox drawer** and slide the drawer back into the box.

3

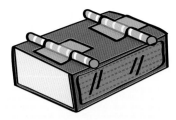

Cut two pieces of the straw. They should both be the **width of the matchbox**. **Tape** these two pieces to the **bottom** of your matchbox, **one near each end**. This is where your wheels are going to go.

4

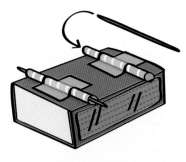

Slide the cocktail sticks **through the straws** so they stick out at both ends. They may be too long, but don't worry – you can trim them soon.

5

Make a **small hole in the middle of each card circle**, then **slide** all four wheels on to the cocktail sticks. You can now trim off any excess bits of stick.

6

Place the car on a **smooth surface** and bring the **other magnet close** to it. It will either move towards the magnet, or be pushed away from it.

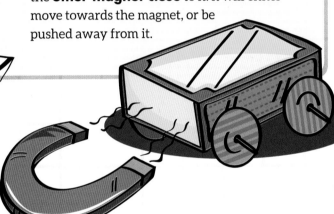

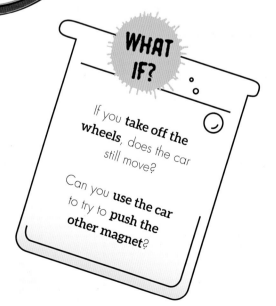

WHAT'S HAPPENING HERE:

The **bar magnets** each have a **north pole** and a **south pole**. When a north and south pole **meet**, they are **attracted to each other**. However, when two of the **same poles meet**, they are **pushed apart**. This invisible **magnetic force** is used to move **some types of train**, so it has no problem pushing along your little matchbox car.

WHAT IF?

If you **take off the wheels**, does the car still move?

Can you **use the car to try to push the other magnet**?

BOTTLE BLAST-OFF!

WHAT YOU'LL NEED:
- Card
- Scissors
- Empty plastic bottle
- Sticky tape
- A foot pump with a needle adaptor
- A cork
- Water

On pages 28–29, we looked at one way to **create a bottle rocket**. That one was pretty messy and out of control. This version is much **less messy**, as it doesn't involve minty diet cola spraying around all over the place, but **should still only be attempted outside**.

WHAT TO DO:

1

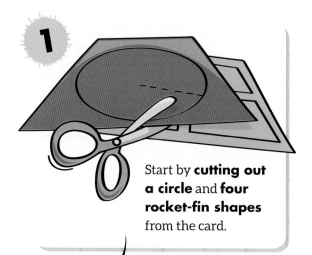

Start by **cutting out a circle** and **four rocket-fin shapes** from the card.

2

Take the lid off your bottle and turn the bottle upside-down. Tape the fins to the spout end of your bottle, and – after cutting a slit in it, from the centre to the edge – twist your circle of card into a cone shape. Tape this to the bottom of your bottle (which is the top of your rocket).

3

Push the **needle adaptor** from the pump all the way through the cork. This will be tricky, so **ask a grown-up to help**.

Fill the bottle about a **third full of water** and put the cork in to **seal** the water inside.

4

Attach the needle adaptor to the pump, then **stand the rocket** on its fins.

5

Pump the foot pump. At first, nothing will happen, but after a little while – **WHOOOSH!** – your rocket will blast off.

WHAT IF?

What if you **don't put water** in the bottle?

Does the **size of the bottle** make a difference?

WHAT'S HAPPENING HERE:

As you pump air into the bottle, the **pressure inside increases**. Eventually, when the bottle can't hold any more pressure, the **cork is forced out**. With nowhere for the cork to go, most of the **energy is directed upwards**, launching the bottle into the air and **spraying water** out behind it like a **rocket's trail**.

BUILD YOUR OWN
SPEEDBOAT

Ever dreamed of owning your own **speedboat**? Well, now you can (sort of)! This experiment is **quick and simple**, and you'll **possibly get wet** . . . so let's dive in.

WHAT YOU'LL NEED:
- A piece of thin card
- A clean plastic bowl or basin
- Water
- Washing-up liquid

WHAT TO DO:

1

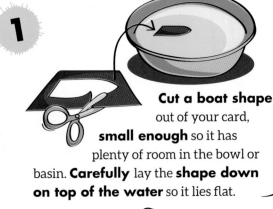

Cut a boat shape out of your card, **small enough** so it has plenty of room in the bowl or basin. **Carefully** lay the **shape down on top of the water** so it lies flat.

2

Place a **blob** of **washing-up liquid** on your finger.

Touch the water behind the boat, then watch it **zoom** across to the other side of the bowl.

WHAT IF?

What happens if you try **adding more washing-up liquid**?

What **other items** can you make float?

WHAT'S HAPPENING HERE:

The boat stays afloat due to the **surface tension** of the water (water molecules sticking together to form a sort of 'skin' on top). By adding the washing-up liquid, **the surface tension behind** the boat **is broken**. The surface tension in **front** of the boat pulls it **forward**.

CHAPTER FOUR
FABULOUS FOOD & DELIGHTFUL DRINK

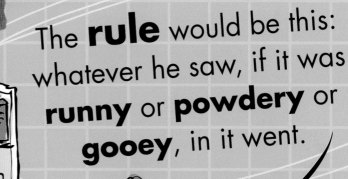

Here are a few **off-the-wall** uses for **food and drink** that even George didn't think of!

The **rule** would be this: whatever he saw, if it was **runny** or **powdery** or **gooey**, in it went.

THE ALL-YELLOW EGG

WHAT TO DO:

1

Place the **uncooked egg** in **one leg** of the tights, around **halfway down**. **Cut off** the other leg if you can. **Wrap elastic bands** on either side of the egg so it can't roll about.

WHAT YOU'LL NEED:

- An egg (uncooked)
- A pair of tights
- Elastic bands
- Water
- A pot

George's medicine doesn't just send Grandma through the roof, it **transforms chickens** to **ten times** their normal size – and it does something extraordinary to their eggs as well! **Now it's your turn.** Everyone knows that once you take the shell off a boiled egg it's white on the outside and yellow on the inside. But did you know **you can turn the whole egg yellow**? Let's get cracking.

2 Using **two hands**, hold the tights at **either end**, leaving **several centimetres** between your hands and the egg.

WHAT'S HAPPENING HERE:

Spinning the egg creates something called **centrifugal force**, which forces the **centre of the object** (in this case, the yolk of the egg) **towards the outside**. This mixes the **yolk and white together**, so once you hard-boil it the egg has turned **completely yellow**. And it's still edible!

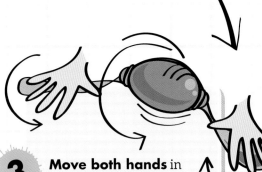

3 **Move both hands** in **small circles**, spinning the egg in front of you. Continue until your arms get tired (or for about four or five minutes).

4 **Ask a grown-up** to **boil the egg** for around **fourteen minutes** – then peel and marvel at your completely yellow egg.

WHAT IF?

What happens if you only **boil the egg** for **four minutes**?

Can you find **another way** to mix the yolk and white together to achieve the **same effect**?

POP
A BALLOON
(BUT NOT IN THE WAY YOU THINK)

There's something **brilliant** about **balloons**. For being nothing more than **thin rubber** stretched over a **load of air**, they're amazingly good fun. It's just a shame that blowing them up is such hard work. Don't worry, though – **science has a solution** that'll save your aching lungs!

WHAT YOU'LL NEED:
- A packet of popping candy
- A balloon
- A small funnel (you can always make your own using card)
- A bottle of fizzy drink
- An elastic band

WHAT TO DO:

1

Pour the **popping candy** into your **uninflated balloon**. This is where the funnel comes in handy.

38

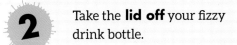

2 Take the **lid off** your fizzy drink bottle.

3

This is a bit fiddly, so you may need help. **Stretch the opening** of the balloon over the **top of the bottle**, making sure none of the popping candy falls into the liquid. The balloon can be **securely** attached using an elastic band.

4

Tip the balloon up so the popping candy **falls** into the drink. The balloon will **inflate** before your very eyes, without you having to huff or puff even once!

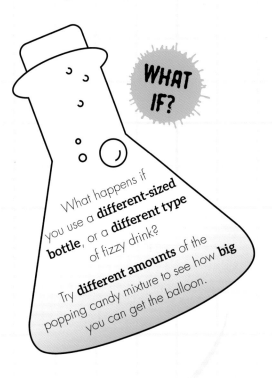

WHAT IF?

What happens if you use a **different-sized bottle**, or a **different type** of fizzy drink? Try **different amounts** of the popping candy mixture to see how **big** you can get the balloon.

WHAT'S HAPPENING HERE:

To understand what's going on, we first have to know what makes **popping candy pop**. If you look very closely at the candy, you'll see it's made up of **thousands of little bubbles**. Each of those bubbles contains **highly compressed carbon dioxide**, which is freed as the candy **dissolves** in your mouth. Dissolving it in the fizzy drink – which is already full of carbon dioxide bubbles – creates a **whoosh of gas** that rises into the balloon, blowing it up.

CRUNCHABLE CANDY CRYSTALS

Learn how to make **delicious crunchy candy crystals** that are both fun to concoct and sweet enough to put a smile on even the most **grizzly** and **grouchy** grandma's face.

WHAT YOU'LL NEED:

- Water (bottled is best)
- A saucepan
- Granulated white sugar
- Food colouring (optional – though it wasn't optional for George, as he had to add brown gloss paint to his medicine to make sure Grandma wasn't suspicious!)
- Flavouring (optional)
- A round-edged wooden ice-lolly stick
- A thick glass jar
- A clothes peg
- Kitchen roll

WHAT TO DO:

1

Ask a grown-up to **heat two cups of water** in a **spotlessly clean saucepan** until it starts to **simmer. Slowly add** four cups of granulated white sugar, a **little** at a time, **stirring** as you go.

2

Stir the water until all of the sugar has **dissolved**. It may be necessary to turn up the heat. Even **a few undissolved grains** will cause the experiment to fail.

3

If you want to add food colouring, pour in several drops now. You can also add flavouring (for example, a dash of fruit juice or a drop of vanilla extract) if you like. **Ask a grown-up to pour the liquid into the glass jar. Be careful, as it will be very hot.**

4

Moisten one half of the ice-lolly stick with water and then **roll it in sugar**. Lower the **coated half of the stick** into the jar, making sure it **doesn't** touch the bottom or sides. Use a **clothes peg** to hold the stick in place.

5

Cover the top of the jar with a sheet of kitchen roll to keep dust out, then **place the jar in a cool, dry place**.

WHAT'S HAPPENING HERE:

When the **water is hot**, it **absorbs more sugar** than it could absorb at room temperature, creating a **super-saturated solution**. As the solution **cools**, the water is unable to hold as much sugar, and the **sugar solidifies again**. The tiny sugar crystals **cling** to any available surface – first your **stick**, and then each other – leaving you with a **delicious sweet treat** to enjoy!

WHAT IF?

Try adding **different flavours** to the sugar-and-water solution.

What happens if you store the jar in **direct sunlight** or on **top of a radiator**?

6

After a few days, **crystals** should start to **form on your stick**. When they don't seem to be growing any bigger, **take the stick out and tuck in**!

INSTANT(ISH) EDIBLE ICE

WHAT YOU'LL NEED:

- A bottle of pure, filtered water
- A bucket tall enough for the bottle to fit inside
- 4kg of ice cubes
- 1.5kg of salt
- Water
- Thermometer
- A glass mixing bowl
- Flavouring (optional)

The **perfect experiment** for a hot summer's day or if you're **bored** one day like George – though with **less explosive results**! Pour a bottle of water into a bowl and it instantly turns to **solid ice**. With a splash of **syrup**, it becomes a **lip-smacking, brain-freezing** treat.

WHAT TO DO:

1

Stand the **bottle** of filtered water **upright in the bucket**. Pack in **most of the ice** around the bottle, **keeping back** five or six cubes in the freezer.

2

Pour **all the salt** over the ice, then **add water** to fill the bucket to the **top of the bottle**.

3

Being careful not to knock the bucket or move the bottle, use the **thermometer** to check the temperature of the water. You want it to go down to around **–8 degrees Celsius**, which should take about **thirty minutes**.

4

Carefully remove the bottle from the bucket. The water inside should still be **liquid**. Place the **reserved ice cubes** in a bowl. Add a **splash of flavouring** on top, if you like.

5

Slowly unscrew the lid of your bottle and pour the water on to the ice cubes. As it hits the ice, the **water freezes instantly**!

WHAT'S HAPPENING HERE:

We all know that **water freezes at zero degrees Celsius**, but because the water we are using in this experiment is **pure and filtered** there are **no impurities** for the ice crystals to cling to, so the water remains **liquid**. As soon as it hits the ice, though, the **freezing process is kick-started**. As the water is **already** so far below freezing point, it **solidifies immediately**.

WHAT IF?

What if, instead of pouring the water out, you bang the **base** of the bottle **hard** on a table?

What happens if you **don't pour salt over the ice**? Why do you think this is?

WORRYINGLY WIGGLY WORMS

Can you believe that **George's grandma** loved to eat **worms** and **slugs** and **beetley bugs**? No wonder he wanted to get rid of her! Here's how you can breathe life into **chewy candy worms**, then horrify your family as they watch them **wriggling** and **squirming** around . . .

WHAT YOU'LL NEED:

- Gummy candy worms
- Two glasses
- Bicarbonate of soda
- Water
- White vinegar

WHAT TO DO:

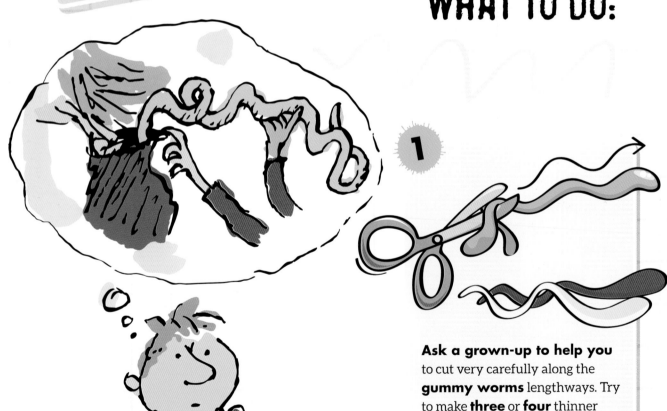

1

Ask a grown-up to help you to cut very carefully along the **gummy worms** lengthways. Try to make **three** or **four** thinner worms from each whole worm.

2

Place your **worm spaghetti** in a glass and add **three tablespoons** of the **bicarbonate of soda**. Pour on enough water so the soda crystals start to **dissolve**, but not so much that all the crystals disappear completely. If you **can't see** any bicarbonate of soda left, just **add some more**.

3

Let the worms **steep** in the solution for **half an hour**. Hum an annoying tune while you wait. **Pour** the vinegar into the **other glass**.

4

Take a **soaked gummy worm** and drop it into the **vinegar**. At first nothing will happen, and you'll think the whole thing has been a massive waste of time – but **wait a few seconds** and the worm will start **wriggling** around like . . . well, like a worm.

WHAT'S HAPPENING HERE:

As we've discovered in earlier experiments, mixing **bicarbonate of soda** with the **acidic vinegar** creates bubbles of **carbon dioxide gas**. Because lots of the soda solution has **soaked** into the gummy worm, **tiny bubbles** form on its **surface** when you drop it in **vinegar**. The bubbles soon grow big enough to **lift the worm**, at which point they escape the worm's sticky grip and **float to the surface**, making the worm **sink** back down again.

WHAT IF?

Try letting the worms **soak** for only a **few minutes**. What happens if you cut the pieces **thinner**, or leave the **worms whole**?

INCREDIBLE INVISIBLE COLA

Mr Kranky is so worked up over George's **magical invention** he puts **butter** in his **coffee** and **milk** on his **toast** and **marmalade** on his **cornflakes**! Did you know that **milk** becomes a **magical ingredient** if you add it to a bottle of cola? It turns the liquid as **clear** as water! George can get it from the cows on his farm, but you've probably got some in your fridge.

WHAT YOU'LL NEED:

- A small bottle of cola
- Semi-skimmed milk
- A notebook or digital camera

WHAT TO DO:

1

Unscrew the cap of your cola bottle and **keep it safe**. **Carefully** – and preferably over a sink – pour in enough semi-skimmed milk to **fill the empty space at the top** of the bottle. You want to fill it to the very **brim**.

2

Screw the top back on the cola bottle, being careful not to shake it up.

3

Keep the bottle on a **level surface** and **check it** every **twenty** to **thirty** minutes. Take a **photograph** or **write** notes each time, describing how it looks.

4

Eventually, all the **milk** will settle to the **bottom** in a **lumpy brown gunge**, leaving the rest of the liquid **completely clear**.

WHAT'S HAPPENING HERE:

The **phosphoric acid molecules** in the cola are **attracted** to the **milk** and **attach** themselves to the milk's molecules the first chance they get. The **milk**, laden with the phosphoric acid molecules, curdles into lumps, which are much heavier than the other liquids in the drink. These **sink** to the bottom, pulling the phosphoric acid – and the brown colour – down with them. The **lighter clear liquids** that are left over then float on top.

WHAT IF?

How about trying a **different** kind of **fizzy drink**?

What happens if you **shake** the separated liquids up to **mix them** again?

47

THE MANY COLOURS OF CABBAGE

WHAT YOU'LL NEED:
- A red cabbage
- A blender
- Three glasses (they need to be REALLY clean)
- Sieve (optional)
- Vinegar
- Washing powder

According to George's grandma, **cabbage** doesn't taste of anything without a few **boiled caterpillars** in it – **slugs**, too! She thinks George should eat mountains of it three times a day, **yuck**! Here's something much more fun you can do with cabbage, and it doesn't involve eating a single piece.

WHAT TO DO:

1

Peel off three or four large **red cabbage leaves** and put them in a blender, **half filled** with water. **Whizz** until the water turns **purple**.

2

Pour **some** of the liquid into **three glasses**. **Sieve out** any **chunks** of cabbage, if necessary. Line the glasses up against a **white background**, as this makes it easier to observe any changes. **Label one glass** as your **colour reference** and leave it untouched.

WHAT'S HAPPENING HERE:

The purple cabbage water **reacts** differently, depending on whether you add an **acidic** substance or an **alkaline** one. **Acids** and **alkalis** are measured on something called a **pH scale**. **Acids** have a **low pH**, while **alkalis** have a **high pH**. The pH of the cabbage water is more or less **neutral** to start with, so adding acid or alkali moves it along the pH scale, and the **pigment** of the water **changes to match** (red indicates an acid; green an alkali).

3

Pour some **vinegar** into one glass and give it a stir. It turns **red**!

4

Tip a **spoonful** of **washing powder** into the second glass and stir. It turns **green**!

WHAT IF?

Try the experiment again with **other additives** – bicarbonate of soda, orange juice, fizzy cola, milk – anything you can think of!

What happens if you **mix** the **red** liquid with the **green** liquid?

WEIRDLY WOBBLY SEE-THROUGH EGG

WHAT TO DO:

1

Place the **egg** in the **bowl**.

Pour in enough **vinegar** to **completely cover** the egg.

2

Leave for **one week**, changing the vinegar on the **second day**.

3

Remove the egg from the bowl and **carefully rinse** in **cold** water ... then be amazed! You can even **bounce** it around (but not too hard or it'll **explode**).

WHAT YOU'LL NEED:

- An egg (uncooked)
- A deep bowl
- White vinegar
- Patience

So you thought that yellow egg experiment on page 36 was impressive? What if, instead of turning an egg yellow, you could **make it see-through?** And **bouncy?** And a bit **weird** – like the **football-sized eggs** caused by George's magic medicine? Well, you can with this **egg-cellent egg-speriment!**

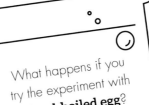

WHAT IF?

What happens if you try the experiment with a **hard-boiled egg?**

Did you notice anything happening to the **size of the egg?** What might cause this?

WHAT'S HAPPENING HERE:

The **acetic acid** in the **vinegar** is reacting with the **calcium carbonate** in the **eggshell**. This makes the **shell dissolve**, but leaves the **membrane inside** the shell unharmed. This membrane gives the egg its **rubbery** consistency and, as the egg is uncooked, the white remains more or less **transparent**.

As George's marvellous mixture begins to **froth** and **foam**, it has an **electrifying effect** on him – and in this chapter you'll discover how to **harness the power** of electricity and magnets!

CHAPTER FIVE
ELECTRIFYING
ELECTRICITY
& MAGNIFICENT
MAGNETS

Whenever he got a **whiff** of it up his nose, **firecrackers** went off in his **skull** and **electric prickles** ran along the backs of his legs.

WIELD THE POWER OF LIGHTNING

WHAT YOU'LL NEED:
- A plastic fork
- Tinfoil
- A rubber glove
- An inflated balloon
- A hairy head
- A wooden or plastic chopping board

Love them or hate them, there's something deeply impressive about **thunderstorms**. All those big **BOOMS** and **flashes** of **electricity** shooting across the sky. It's pretty dramatic stuff. What if you could **create lightning** of your own . . . ?

WHAT TO DO:

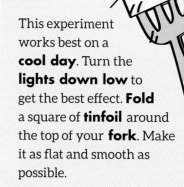

1

This experiment works best on a **cool day**. Turn the **lights down low** to get the best effect. **Fold** a square of **tinfoil** around the top of your **fork**. Make it as flat and smooth as possible.

2

Wearing the rubber glove, rub the **balloon** against your **hair** for one minute. **Do not touch** the balloon with your **bare hand**, or you'll have to start all over again.

3

Place the **balloon** on the **chopping board**. Holding the **fork** in your **gloved hand**, touch it to the balloon and **hold** it there.

4

With your **bare hand**, touch a **finger to the foil**. You will see (and feel) a **spark**. Don't worry – it won't hurt!

WHAT'S HAPPENING HERE:

By **rubbing the balloon** against your **hair**, you are **adding electrons** to it, which charges it up with **static electricity**. Electrons have a **negative electrical charge** and are attracted to **protons**, which have a **positive electrical charge**. When you touch the **tinfoil-covered fork** to the **balloon**, the fork is suddenly overfilled with **electrons** it can't get rid of. That is, until you bring your **finger close enough**. Once you do, the electrons **jump** to your skin – which is an **excellent conductor** – before **zooming** through your body and **discharging** harmlessly into the ground.

WHAT IF?

After you've made the **first spark**, **lift** the fork away and **touch it again**. What happens?

With the **lights off**, bring your finger **close** to the tinfoil **without touching** it. Can you see anything?

A MOST EXCELLENT ELECTRIFIED MAGNET

Put **electricity** and **magnets together** and what have you got? An **electromagnet**, just like this one.

WHAT YOU'LL NEED:
- 3–4 metres of insulated copper wire
- Wire strippers
- An iron nail (the longer, the better)
- A large D-size battery

WHAT TO DO:

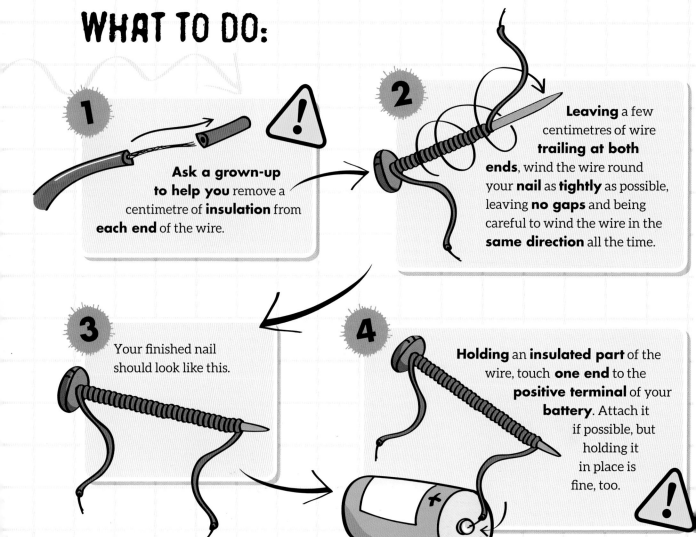

1 **Ask a grown-up to help you** remove a centimetre of **insulation** from **each end** of the wire.

2 **Leaving** a few centimetres of wire **trailing at both ends**, wind the wire round your **nail** as **tightly** as possible, leaving **no gaps** and being careful to wind the wire in the **same direction** all the time.

3 Your finished nail should look like this.

4 **Holding** an **insulated part** of the wire, touch **one end** to the **positive terminal** of your **battery**. Attach it if possible, but holding it in place is fine, too.

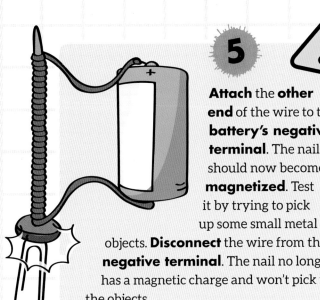

5

Attach the **other end** of the wire to the **battery's negative terminal**. The nail should now become **magnetized**. Test it by trying to pick up some small metal objects. **Disconnect** the wire from the **negative terminal**. The nail no longer has a magnetic charge and won't pick up the objects.

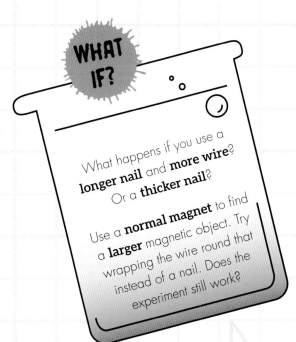

WHAT IF?

What happens if you use a **longer nail** and **more wire**? Or a **thicker nail**?

Use a **normal magnet** to find a **larger** magnetic object. Try wrapping the wire round that instead of a nail. Does the experiment still work?

WHAT'S HAPPENING HERE:

When you **connect** the **wire** to **both** battery terminals, an **electrical current** flows through the wire. A flowing electrical current produces a small **magnetic field**, which is **amplified** by having the wire **wound so tightly** round the nail. This, in turn, makes the nail **magnetic**. When the battery is **disconnected** and the flow stops, the magnetic field **stops**, too, and the nail becomes just a boring old nail again.

RETURN OF THE MAGNETIC CAR

On pages 30–31 we looked at how to build a **magnetic car**. Let's look at another way to do it that is **simpler** but even **more impressive**.

On pages 30–31

WHAT YOU'LL NEED:

- One AA battery
- Two circular magnets (hint: check the back of your fridge magnets – but ask permission from whoever owns the magnets before taking them apart!)
- Tinfoil

WHAT TO DO:

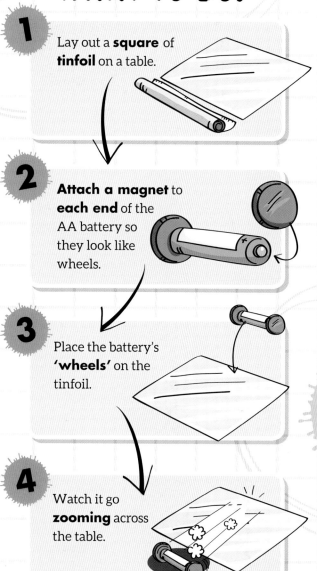

1 Lay out a **square** of **tinfoil** on a table.

2 **Attach a magnet** to **each end** of the AA battery so they look like wheels.

3 Place the battery's **'wheels'** on the tinfoil.

4 Watch it go **zooming** across the table.

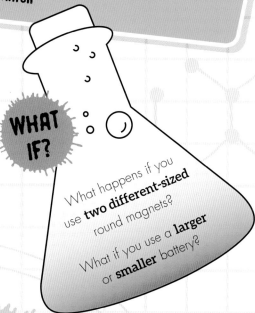

WHAT IF?

What happens if you use **two different-sized** round magnets?

What if you use a **larger** or **smaller** battery?

WHAT'S HAPPENING HERE:

The **battery moves** due to something called **Lorentz force**. The **electricity** in the battery is creating a **magnetic field**. The **tinfoil**, meanwhile, is acting as a **conductor** and, because of the positioning of the battery-and-magnet car on the foil, it creates **torque** – which is just another way of saying it makes the **magnets spin**.

THE MIRACULOUS BENDING WATER

All Grandma's talk of **gobbling live slugs** and **big fat earwigs** makes George wonder if she's actually a **witch**. In this experiment, you might just convince your friends that you're some kind of **witch** or **wizard**, but you don't have to eat any **creepy-crawlies** to do it. You just need to **bend some water** . . . .

WHAT YOU'LL NEED:
- A plastic comb
- A bathroom or kitchen tap
- A hairy head

WHAT TO DO:

1 **Turn** the **tap on** and adjust until the **flow** is as **thin** as possible **without spluttering**.

2 **Comb** your hair **ten** to **twenty times**.

3 **Hold** the comb **parallel** with the **flowing water** and slowly **move it closer**. The water should **curve** towards it, as if by **magic**.

WHAT IF?

Can you **replicate the experiment** using a **balloon** instead of a comb?

Does the experiment work if you wear a **rubber glove** on the **hand holding** the comb?

WHAT'S HAPPENING HERE:

Combing your hair is **charging** the plastic comb with **negatively charged electrons**. As you bring the comb **closer** to the water, the **positively charged protons** in it are **drawn towards** the **electrons** in the comb.

MUNCHABLE METAL

WHAT YOU'LL NEED:
- A bowl of simple breakfast cereal (check the ingredients to make sure it contains iron)
- A sealable transparent sandwich bag
- Warm water
- A strong magnet

Some of the ingredients in George's marvellous medicine are enough to make your eyes water, like **DISHWORTH'S FAMOUS DANDRUFF CURE** or **BRILLIDENT FOR CLEANING FALSE TEETH**! It's a good job Grandma doesn't ask to see an ingredients list before she drinks it . . .

Have you ever read the list of **ingredients** on your **cereal boxes** in the morning? Some breakfast cereals claim they're 'fortified with iron'? Surely they can't mean real iron, though, can they? Let's try and find out.

WHAT TO DO:

1

Place a **cupful of cereal** in the bag. **Pour** in **warm water** until the bag is **half full**.

2

Seal the bag, leaving a **pocket of air** inside. **Shake** the bag for a **few seconds**. You'll see the warm water start to **dissolve** the cereal.

3

Leave the bag for around **twenty minutes** so the water and cereal turn into a disgusting-looking **cereal soup. Holding** the **magnet flat** in one hand, **lay** the bag on **top** of it.

4

Move the **magnet** around **slowly**, being careful to ensure it **stays in contact** with the bag at all times.

5

After a few minutes, **tip the bag** – keeping the magnet in place – then **drag** the magnet **up to the air-filled part**.

6

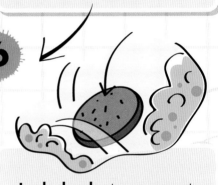

Look closely at your magnet. See all those little **black dots**? That's the **metal** you munch every morning when you eat your breakfast!

WHAT'S HAPPENING HERE:

All of us already have bits of **iron** whizzing around inside us. In fact, there's enough iron in the average person to make one **large nail** – which is good, because we need **iron in our blood to be healthy**. The iron in breakfast cereal is **perfectly safe** to eat and is gradually **absorbed into your bloodstream** through your stomach.

WHAT IF?

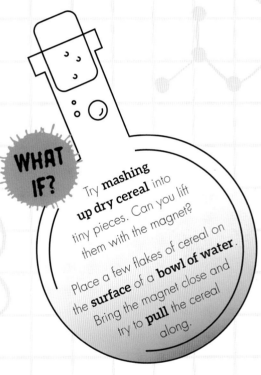

Try **mashing up dry cereal** into tiny pieces. Can you lift them with the magnet?

Place a few flakes of cereal on the **surface** of a **bowl of water**. Bring the magnet close and try to **pull** the cereal along.

THE **POWER OF POTATOES**

Whether **chomping** them as **chips** or **munching** them as **mash**, most of us are partial to the odd potato. But did you know that **potatoes are electric**? If George didn't have a battery for his clock, he might have **dug** one up on the farm and **powered** it like this, instead.

WHAT YOU'LL NEED:

- Two large baking potatoes
- Two large galvanized nails
- Two short lengths of thick copper wire – 3–5 cm will do
- Six crocodile clips
- Three insulated electrical wires
- A battery-operated clock with battery removed

WHAT TO DO:

1

First of all, **mark one potato** with a '**+**' sign and **the other** with a '**–**' sign. **Insert** a **galvanized nail halfway** into each potato.

2

At the **opposite end** of each potato – **as far away** from the nail as possible – insert the **thick copper wire**.

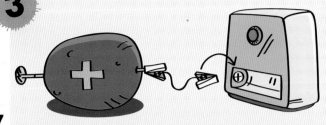

3

Attach the **crocodile clips** to the wires, so each wire has a **clip at each end**. Connect a **crocodile clip** to the **copper wire** on your '**+**' potato. Connect **the other end** of the wire to the '**+**' (positive) **terminal** of your **clock**.

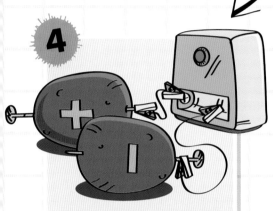

4

Connect another insulated wire between the galvanized nail on your '**–**' **potato** and the '**–**' (negative) **terminal** of the **clock**.

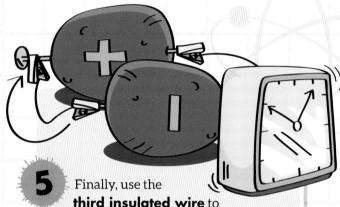

5

Finally, use the **third insulated wire** to connect the **copper wire** of the '**–**' **potato** to the **galvanized nail** of your '**+**' potato. The **clock** will start to **tick**!

WHAT'S HAPPENING HERE:

Wiring up your **potatoes** has turned them into an **electrochemical battery** – a battery in which the power is generated by **chemical energy turning into electrical energy**. **Zinc** in the galvanized **nails** reacts with the **copper wire**, causing **electrons** to flow through the potatoes and along the wires, **powering the clock**.

WHAT IF?

Set the clock to the **correct time** and watch to see how long it takes to **fall behind**.

Do **other vegetables** give the same result?

SHINE
A LIGHT ON
STATIC
ELECTRICITY

We powered a clock with potatoes on page 60, but did you know you can also **power a light** with a **single balloon**? It's all thanks to the wonders of **static electricity**.

WHAT YOU'LL NEED:
- An inflated balloon
- A hairy head
- A fluorescent light bulb (those long thin ones)

WHAT TO DO:

1

Rub the **inflated balloon** against your **head** for thirty to sixty seconds.

2

With the **lights out, touch the metal prongs** of the **fluorescent light bulb** to the **balloon** (being careful not to push so hard that the balloon pops).

3

The **bulb** will **illuminate**. Rub the balloon against your hair for longer for a more dramatic effect.

WHAT'S HAPPENING HERE:

We already know that rubbing a balloon against your hair charges it with **negative electrons**. When the **bulb's prongs** both touch the **balloon**, it **creates an electrical circuit** for the electrons to flow through. **Inside** the bulb is **mercury gas** and, when the electrons from the balloon **bump** into the electrons from the gas, they release **photons**. It is these photons that make the **bulb glow**.

WHAT IF?

How long can you make the **bulb glow** for?

Does a **smaller bulb** light up **brighter**, or appear more **dim**?

CHAPTER SIX
QUICK 'N' EASY

'**Don't** keep saying **wait a minute!**' shouted Mr Kranky. 'There isn't a minute to wait! **We must get cracking at once!**'

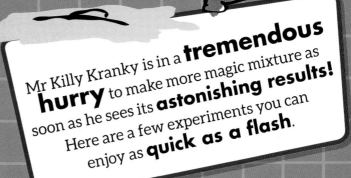

Mr Killy Kranky is in a **tremendous hurry** to make more magic mixture as soon as he sees its **astonishing results!** Here are a few experiments you can enjoy as **quick as a flash**.

LOVELY LAVA LAMP 1

WHAT YOU'LL NEED:
- A clear plastic bottle
- Water
- Food colouring
- Vegetable oil
- Salt

George's **magic mixture** is a sight to behold, **bubbling** and **frothing** and **foaming** as though it were alive. Here's an **exciting mixture** you can make at home, if you've ever wanted a **lava lamp** but don't fancy paying all that money for it. There are **two options** for making your own.

WHAT TO DO:

1 **Remove** the **bottle top** and pour **water** into the bottle until it is **almost full**. **Sprinkle** in a few drops of **food colouring**.

Add three to five tablespoons of vegetable oil.

2 **Sprinkle** on **salt** until the oil **bubbles start to sink**, then watch them **bob back upwards again**, just like a real lava lamp.

WHAT'S HAPPENING HERE:

Oil and water are **immiscible liquids**, which means they **won't mix together**, no matter how hard you might try to make them. When you add the **salt**, it **clings** to the **oil**, dragging it down to the bottom of the bottle. As it falls, the **salt dissolves** in the water. The oil, which is now **lighter** than water, **floats back** to the top again.

WHAT IF?

Try the experiment with **two bottles** – one filled with **icy cold water**, and the other with **warm water**. Is there a **difference** in how the **oil reacts**?

What happens if you use **less water** and **more oil** in your mix?

LOVELY LAVA LAMP 2

Did that last **lava lamp** seem like too much effort? Try this **hassle-free version**.

WHAT YOU'LL NEED:
- A half-empty bottle of cola (or half-full, depending on your mood)
- Vegetable oil
- Alka-Seltzer or dissolvable aspirin tablet

WHAT TO DO:

1  **Carefully** pour the oil **into** the bottle so it **sits on top** of the cola.

2 **Drop in half** an Alka-Seltzer or dissolvable aspirin tablet.

3  Watch the **bubbles** slowly **rise** through the oil.

WHAT IF?

What happens if you use **water mixed with food colouring** instead of the cola?

Does the experiment work if you put the **lid back on the bottle**?

WHAT'S HAPPENING HERE:

Just like with water, **oil refuses to mix with cola**. When you drop in the tablet, it **creates carbon dioxide bubbles in the cola**, adding to those already there. These bubbles of cola are **lighter** than the oil, so **rise slowly** until they reach the top. At the **top**, the **gas escapes** and the **cola sinks** back down again.

COLOUR-CHANGING CARNATIONS

WHAT YOU'LL NEED:
- Drinking glasses
- Water
- White flowers (roses, carnations or even large garden daisies will all work)
- Food colouring (a variety of colours)

White flowers are OK, but have you ever wished they could be more **colourful**? This experiment will show you how to go about **colouring white flowers** any way you like, and you certainly **won't need** brown shoe polish or dark-brown gloss paint like George to achieve it!

WHAT TO DO:

1

Pour water into your glasses and add a **different colour** of food colouring to **each glass**.

2

Cut your flowers so the **stems** are just a **few centimetres longer** than each glass. Place **one** or **two** flowers in each glass.

WHAT IF?

Ask a **grown-up** to help you carefully **slit one stem in half lengthways** and position the two half-stems (of the one flower) in two glasses filled with **different** coloured water. What happens? What if you use a **yellow** or **pink** flower instead of a white one?

3

In an **hour** or **two**, you'll start to notice a **change of colour**, which will increase over the next few days.

WHAT'S HAPPENING HERE:

The **colour of flowers** is **partly determined** by the **soil** they are planted in and the **water** they drink. In this case, your flowers are **drinking the coloured water** (you may even be able to see it passing up the stem!) and the colouring is then being **absorbed** by the petals.

BEND A BONE

'Never grow up,' Grandma tells George, **'always down'** – which is quite an impossible thing to achieve as **bones** like to grow **bigger**! But did you know there is a way to make a **bone bendy**? Here's how . . .

WHAT YOU'LL NEED:

- A bone (such as a chicken leg bone)
- A glass jar big enough for the bone to fit in, with a lid
- Vinegar
- Patience

WHAT TO DO:

1

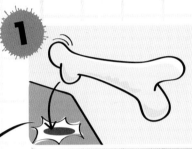

Take your **bone** and **clean it thoroughly** to get **rid** of any **meat**. **Test** the bone to make sure it's **solid**. Try **bending** it. **Gently tap** it on a table. Take note of how it feels.

2

Place the bone in the **jar** and **fill it to the top** with the **vinegar**. **Screw on** the lid.

3

Wait three to four days, then take the bone out and **rinse it** under the tap.

4

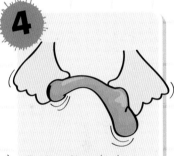

Try **bending** the bone and see what happens.

WHAT'S HAPPENING HERE:

Calcium is that **magic ingredient** that gives **bones** their **strength**. The **acid** in the **vinegar**, although quite mild, is enough to **dissolve** all the bone's **calcium molecules**, leaving nothing but the more **pliable bone tissue** behind.

WHAT IF?

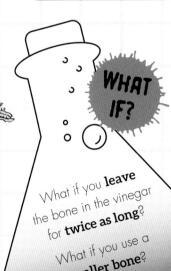

What if you **leave** the bone in the vinegar for **twice as long**?

What if you use a **smaller bone**?

RAINBOW RAIN

Grandma's **new improved medicine** makes her **bulge** and **swell** and turns her face from **purple to green**! You can create something much prettier in this experiment – **rainbow rain**!

WHAT YOU'LL NEED:

- A large jar or glass jug
- Water
- White shaving foam
- Drinking glasses
- Food colouring (a variety of colours)
- An eyedropper (optional)

WHAT TO DO:

1 Fill the jar **two-thirds** full with **water**. Squirt **shaving foam** on top of the water, so it looks like a **cloud**.

2 In the **drinking glasses**, mix up some more **water** and different colours of **food colouring**.

3 **Slowly** and **carefully pour** (or, better still, use an eyedropper to drip) the **coloured water** on to the **foam**.

4 The **shaving foam fills up** until it can't hold the coloured water any longer, then lets it **fall like rain** into the water below.

68

WHAT'S HAPPENING HERE:

What's happening here is more or less exactly what happens **in the sky** on a **rainy day**. **Real clouds** are made up of **water vapour** mixed with **air**. The **more moisture** is added, the **larger** the **droplets** of water vapour become. Eventually, the size and weight of the water droplets is **too much** for the air to hold on to, and it **falls as rain**. In this experiment, the **foam is the air**, and by adding lots of water droplets the foam eventually can't hold on to them all any longer.

WHAT IF?

What if you used **vegetable oil under your cloud** instead of water?

What if, rather than the **coloured water**, you dripped a **fizzy drink** into the foam?

AWESOMELY DESTRUCTIVE AIR

We may not be able to see it or touch it, but **air** is **all around us all the time**. Unless we're underwater, or in space, in which case it isn't. Assuming you're neither of those things, though, let's take a look at how **powerful air** can be.

WHAT YOU'LL NEED:

- A large plastic bottle
- Hot water
- A large bowl
- Cold water
- Ice

WHAT TO DO:

1 With a grown-up's **help**, **pour** hot water into the bottle until it's about **half full**. Leave it to **stand** for a few minutes.

2 **Put the lid** on the bottle and **lay it on its side** in the bowl.

3 **Pour** ice and cold water over it.

4 **After a minute or so**, stand the bottle up. It will begin to **crush itself** before your very eyes!

WHAT IF?

What if you use a **small plastic bottle** instead of a large one?

Does the bottle still get **crushed** if you leave the **hot water to cool on its own**, without adding ice and cold water?

WHAT'S HAPPENING HERE:

As the **hot water cools**, it **reduces the pressure** of the air inside the bottle. Air likes to move from **high-pressure areas to low-pressure areas** (to balance the pressure), so, once the level of air pressure inside the bottle drops below that outside the bottle, **the air outside tries to get inside** – but the plastic gets in the way, and is crumpled.

TWIRLY SWIRLY ART SHOW

WHAT YOU'LL NEED:
- A plate
- Milk
- Food colouring (a variety of colours)
- Washing-up liquid

As you know by now, **George Kranky** created a **phenomenally potent** magic mixture – he even thought he saw **bright sparks flashing** in the **swirling foam**! Now you can create your own **moving liquid paintings** without having to pick up a brush.

WHAT TO DO:

1 **Pour enough milk** on to the plate to **cover the bottom** with a **thin layer**. Drip a few different drops of **food colouring** into the **middle** of the milk. Try to get them close together **without any overlapping and mixing**.

2 Taking **careful aim**, squeeze a **single squirt** of **washing-up liquid** into the middle of the food colouring.

3 The colours will **shoot** across the **surface of the milk**, swirling together into **patterns**.

WHAT IF?

If you add a **second drop** of **washing-up liquid** to the patterns, does anything happen? Why do you think this is?

What happens if you put the **washing-up liquid** and **food colouring** on the **plate first**, then add the milk?

WHAT'S HAPPENING HERE:

Just like with the speedboat experiment on page 34, the **washing-up liquid** is breaking down the **surface tension** of the milk. As it does, the **stronger** surface tension on **all sides** of the plate **pulls the milk and food colouring along**, creating a colourful pattern.

ULTIMATE
UNDERWATER
VOLCANO

WHAT TO DO:

WHAT YOU'LL NEED:
- String
- A small bottle
- A large jug
- Cold water
- Hot water
- Red food colouring

As you've seen, all sorts of things can be used to **explode liquid** from bottles, or in George Kranky's case, nearly **explode** a certain **grouchy grandma**! Whether it's **vinegar** and **bicarbonate of soda**, **Mentos mints** and **cola**, or just a **foot pump** and a lot of effort, liquid has erupted all over the place. Let's finish the way we started – with a **volcano**.

1 Take a **piece of string** and tie **both ends** round the **neck of your bottle** to make a **looped handle**. This should be long enough to lower your bottle all the way to the bottom of the jug (but don't do that yet).

2 **Pour cold water** into the jug until it's deep enough to **completely submerge** the bottle, with **room left over**.

3 **Carefully pour hot water** into the bottle. Add enough **food colouring** so the water turns a **vibrant shade of red**.

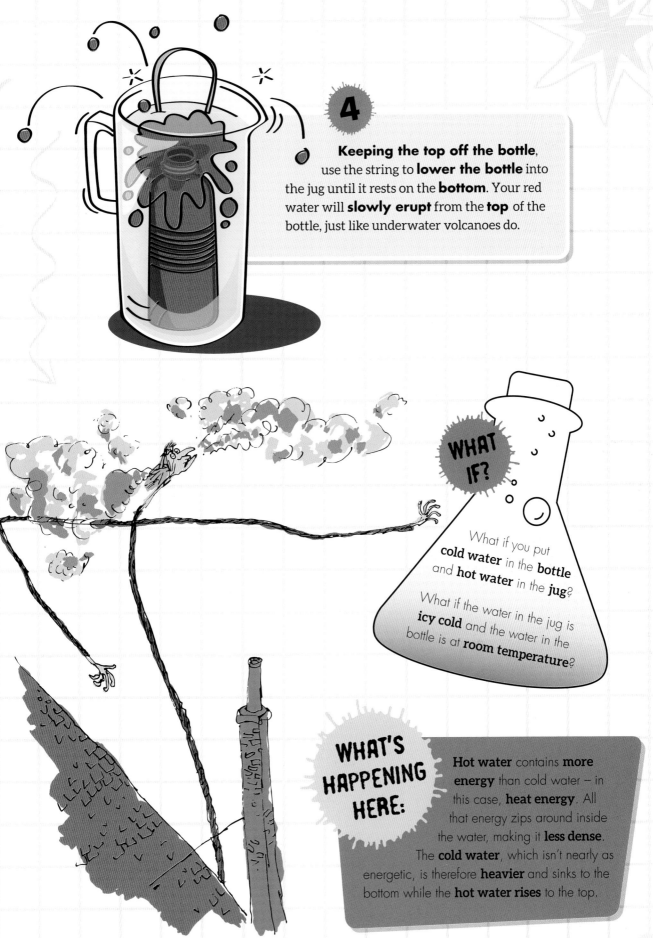

4

Keeping the top off the bottle, use the string to **lower the bottle** into the jug until it rests on the **bottom**. Your red water will **slowly erupt** from the **top** of the bottle, just like underwater volcanoes do.

WHAT IF?

What if you put **cold water** in the **bottle** and **hot water** in the **jug**?

What if the water in the jug is **icy cold** and the water in the bottle is at **room temperature**?

WHAT'S HAPPENING HERE:

Hot water contains **more energy** than cold water – in this case, **heat energy**. All that energy zips around inside the water, making it **less dense**. The **cold water**, which isn't nearly as energetic, is therefore **heavier** and sinks to the bottom while the **hot water rises** to the top.

NOTES

HOW MANY HAVE YOU READ?

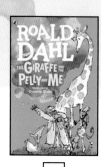
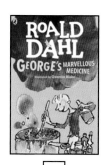

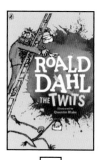

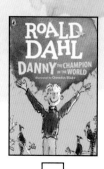
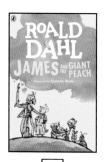
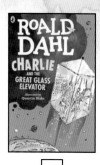

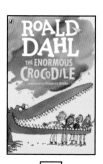

FEWER THAN 5? WHOOPSY-SPLUNKERS! You've got some reading to do!

BETWEEN 5 AND 10? Wonderful surprises await! Keep reading . . .

MORE THAN 10? Whoopee! Which was your favourite?